P9-EEU-167

Life in the Ocean

by Della Cohen

design & illustrations by Nancee McClure

 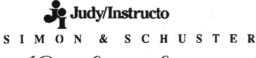
Judy/Instructo

SIMON & SCHUSTER

A Paramount Communications Company

Published by Judy/Instructo, Minneapolis, MN 55406

Entire contents copyright © 1991 Judy/Instructo, part of the Education Group of Simon & Schuster, a Paramount Communications company. However, the individual purchaser may reproduce designated materials in this book for classroom and individual use, but the purchase of this book does not entitle reproduction of any part for an entire school, district, or system. Such use is strictly prohibited.

ISBN 0 - 382 - 29818 - 7

Printed in the United States of America

Table of Contents

Introduction

Use this book of reproducibles to supplement your lessons about the world's oceans. The activities focus on people and how they use products and food from the sea, how they make their living engaged in sea-related occupations, and how they affect the sea in both negative and positive ways. Three special features are included:

1. A three-page vertical poster, **2.** A thirteen-page booklet about mammals of the sea and **3.** A group of special projects using sea animal cutouts. Depending on students' abilities, some will be able to complete these activities by themselves and others will need guidance.

Teaching Tips

The majority of the pages are self-explanatory. Below are some additional suggestions.

Pages 7-8. Display a globe and challenge students to locate the oceans and seas. Instead of having children glue the hemisphere pieces back-to-back, you might have cotton available for students to stuff between the two parts and then staple them together. This will give dimension and provide a more interesting globe for your students to enjoy.

Pages 12-14. Help students read the labels on the poster. Then help them cut out the poster parts and glue the parts together on the bottom strips (as indicated). Point out to students that sunlight reaches only about 300 feet down. The deeper one goes into the ocean the darker it becomes. To make this point, have students use a light blue crayon to color the background of the Sunlight Zone, a deeper blue for the Twilight Zone, and black for the Dark Zone. Explain to students that many of the fish and other animals that live in the bottom of the sea make their own light. Some have chemicals in their bodies that make the light; others have bacteria that light up. Children might enjoy coloring these animals with hot pink, green and red metallic crayons.

Pages 32-44. Help children cut out and collate their *Mammals of the Sea* booklets. Read the written material with them. Explain that the information given here about each animal is a brief summary. There are always more things to learn about sea mammals. On the lines provided, encourage children to practice writing the name of the animal. More able students might write a few descriptive words on the lines, too.

Pages 45-48. Special Projects for Sea Animal Cutouts

1. To make a durable set of sea animals, color each animal using bright colored crayons, markers or paints. Glue the animals on card-sized pieces of colored construction paper or tagboard, and laminate. Show the children how to play "Concentration" with the cards, or remove one card from the batch and show them how to play a version of "Old Maid."

2. Use as many class periods as necessary to allow children to color and cut out their cards. Enlarging the cards on a copy machine will make coloring easier for the children. For more durability, you might help children paste the animal cutouts onto tagboard before coloring and cutting. Have children work in pairs to help each other read the animal name labels on the cards. More able students might learn to spell the names on the cards as well.

3. Some children might make mobiles with the cards. Provide string, a hole punch, and a hanger. Help children tie the string to the cards and attach to the hanger. Display the mobiles in the classroom or have children take them home.

4. Children can glue straws or ice cream sticks on the back of some cards and use them as stick puppets for extemporaneous puppet shows and discussions about life in the ocean. You might want to use the poster featured on pages 12-14 as a backdrop for the children's presentations.

Listen/Read

What is the Ocean?

Most of planet Earth is covered by water. There are four oceans in the world. They are, from largest to smallest: the Pacific Ocean, the Atlantic Ocean, the Indian Ocean, and the Arctic Ocean. The Pacific Ocean is the deepest. The deepest part of the Pacific would cover the tallest skyscraper or the tallest mountain. The Atlantic Ocean is not as deep as the Indian Ocean. The Arctic Ocean is the shallowest ocean. All ocean water is salty.

Another word for *ocean* is *sea*. The word *sea* can be confusing because there are smaller bodies of salty water, that are not oceans, which are called seas. Some of these are the Red Sea, the Black Sea, and the Mediterranean Sea.

Oceans and seas are very important, not only to the many plants and animals that live in them, but also to the people who live on this planet.

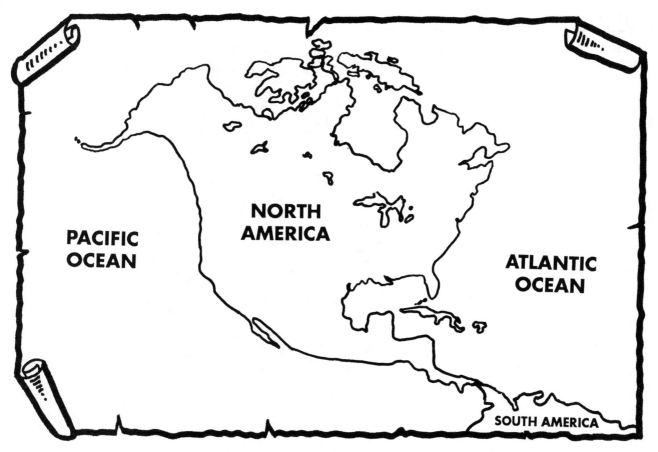

5

JI 8690 © 1991 Judy/Instructo, Minneapolis, MN 55406

Try It

What Does Ocean Water Taste Like?

You need:

1 cup of water
1 teaspoon salt
1 teaspoon

You do:
1. Add 1 teaspoon of salt to the cup of water.
2. Stir.
3. Taste a small bit of the water.
   Tell how it tastes.

Talk About It

How is ocean water different from water in lakes and rivers?

What kind of water do you drink?

6

JI 8690 © 1991 Judy/Instructo, Minneapolis, MN 55406

Where is the Land? Where is the Water?

(Use with page 8.)

Color in the boxes that contain the names of the oceans.
Color the oceans blue.
Color the lands brown.
Then cut along
the dotted
lines.

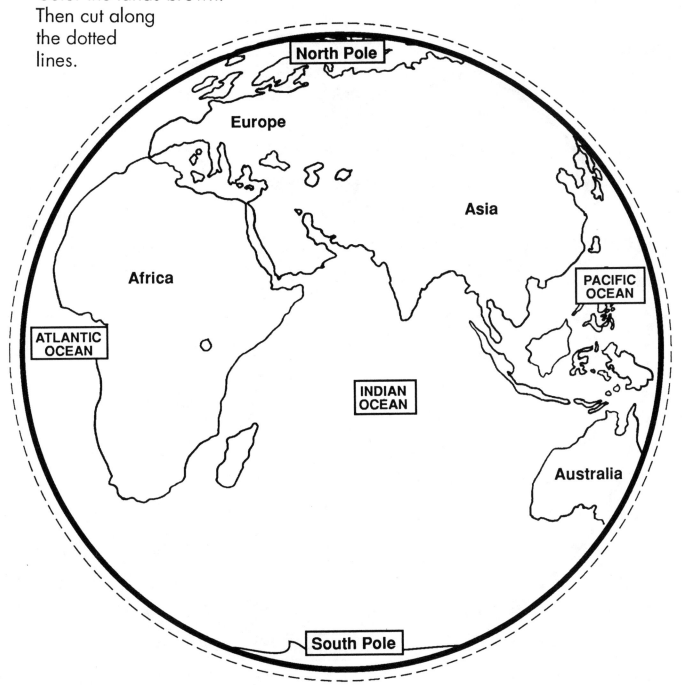

JI 8690 © 1991 Judy/Instructo, Minneapolis, MN 55406

Where is the Land? Where is the Water?

(Use with page 7.)

Color in the boxes that contain the names of the oceans.
Color the oceans blue.
Color the lands brown.
Then cut along the
dotted lines.
Glue the two
parts of the
world
together.

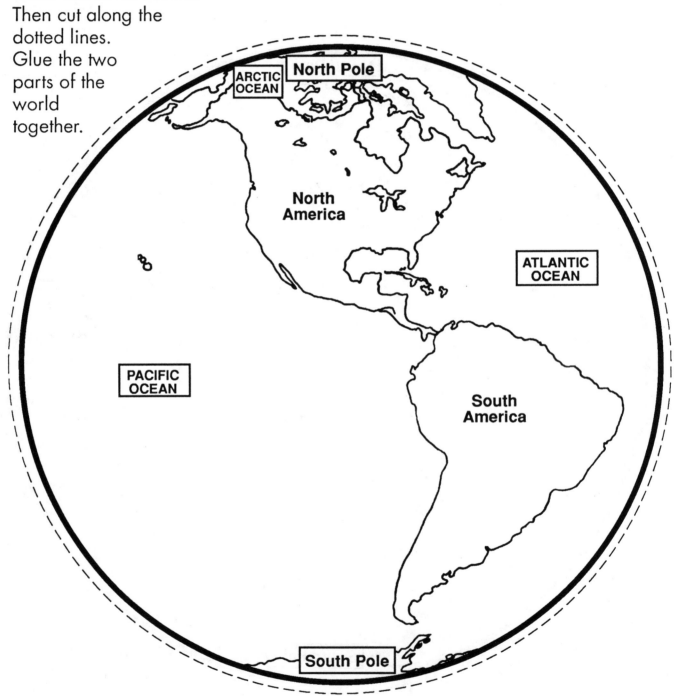

JI 8690 © 1991 Judy/Instructo, Minneapolis, MN 55406

Sea Plants

Many kinds of plants live in the ocean.

Some plants are so tiny you need a microscope to see them.

phytoplankton

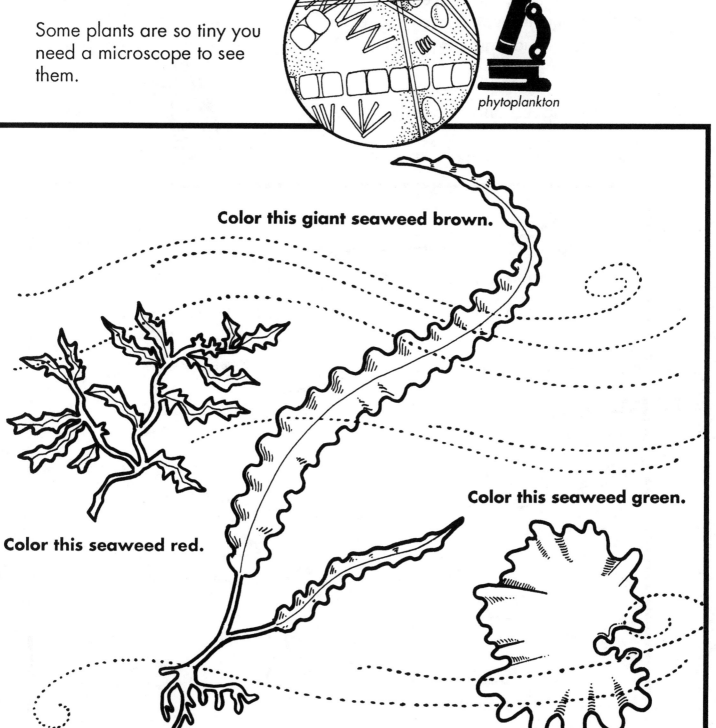

Color this giant seaweed brown.

Color this seaweed green.

Color this seaweed red.

JI 8690 © 1991 Judy/Instructo, Minneapolis, MN 55406

Sea Animals

Many kinds of animals live in the ocean.

Some animals are so tiny you can
see them only through a microscope.
Other sea animals are larger and
live in the ocean.

Color the biggest animal blue.

Color the smallest animal grey.

zooplankton

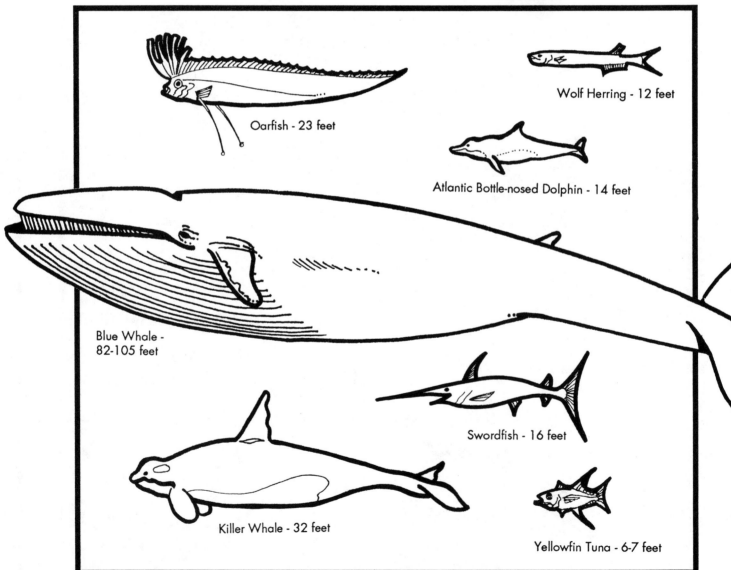

Oarfish - 23 feet

Wolf Herring - 12 feet

Atlantic Bottle-nosed Dolphin - 14 feet

Blue Whale -
82-105 feet

Swordfish - 16 feet

Killer Whale - 32 feet

Yellowfin Tuna - 6-7 feet

10

JI 8690 © 1991 Judy/Instructo, Minneapolis, MN 55406

Strange But True

Sea Anemones

These look like pretty flowers but they are not plants. They are animals called **sea anemones**. They eat small fish that they catch in their petal-like arms.

Find and color the two anemones that are exactly alike.

JI 8690 © 1991 Judy/Instructo, Minneapolis, MN 55406

Make a Poster (Use with pages 13 and 14.)

These plants and animals live near the water's surface.
Color them. Then listen to your teacher's directions.

THE SUNLIGHT ZONE

Atlantic flyingfish

dolphin

zooplankton

Portugese man-of-war

hammerhead shark

cushion star

yellowfin tuna

sea turtle

sea urchin

starfish

mackerel

Glue The Twilight Zone here.

12

JI 8690 © 1991 Judy/Instructo, Minneapolis, MN 55406

Make a Poster *(Use with pages 12 and 14.)*

These animals live deeper beneath the sea. Some sunlight reaches these waters, but the light is dim.
Color the animals. Then listen to your teacher's directions.

THE TWILIGHT ZONE

sperm whale

white shark

squid

octopus

lanternfish

clam

scallop

deep-sea snake mackerel

Glue The Darkness Zone here.

JI 8690 © 1991 Judy/Instructo, Minneapolis, MN 55406

Make a Poster (Use with pages 12 and 13.)

These animals live where sunlight cannot reach. No plants can grow here.
Some of the animals use chemicals in their bodies to make their own light.
Color the animals. Then listen to your teacher's directions.

THE DARKNESS ZONE

deep sea shark

swivel-toothed dragonfish

luminescent squid

anglerfish

deep-sea jellyfish

oarfish

brittle stars

rattail

sea lilies

sea urchins

sea cucumbers

venus flower baskets

14

JI 8690 © 1991 Judy/Instructo, Minneapolis, MN 55406

Pollution

When people pollute, they make the world around them dirty and unhealthy. Our oceans become polluted because some people throw trash into the sea rather than recycle or use a wastebasket.

Color the ocean blue and green.

What do you think?
Answer the question.
What should this boy do with his soda can and napkin?

_____

- -

_____

- -

_____

JI 8690 © 1991 Judy/Instructo, Minneapolis, MN 55406

Pollution

Oil is very bad for sea animals and the environment. Sometimes oil tankers get into accidents. The tanker might run into an iceberg or a pier. If the tanker is badly damaged, oil can spill into the sea. The oil is heavy. It can prevent a seabird from flying and a sea animal from swimming. The animals try to clean themselves. But they become sick when they swallow the oil. Some animals die.

Many people work to clean up oil spills. They help clean the animals so that they can fly and swim again.

Color the picture of people cleaning up the oil spill.

JI 8690 © 1991 Judy/Instructo, Minneapolis, MN 55406

Make a Poster

Show how people can keep our waters clean.

Keep Our Waters Clean

JI 8690 © 1991 Judy/Instructo, Minneapolis, MN 55406

Let's Go to the Beach

Look at the top picture. Then look at the bottom picture and mark 5 things that are different from the one above.

Which beach would you like to visit? Tell why.

JI 8690 © 1991 Judy/Instructo, Minneapolis, MN 55406

Listen/Read

Too Much!

Some fish eat other fish. Cod, for example, eat herring. Some fishermen had been taking too many herring from the sea. Then the cod fish did not have enough to eat.

Now there are laws to protect the fish. Fish must have time to lay eggs. The eggs must hatch. The fish must have time to grow before fishermen fill their nets.

JI 8690 © 1991 Judy/Instructo, Minneapolis, MN 55406

Name_____

Let's Go Fishing!

Have you ever gone fishing? Did you follow the rules about throwing back a fish that is too small?
Use a ruler or a piece of string. Find and color the flounder that are larger than this one.

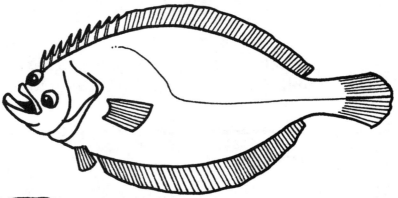

20

JI 8690 © 1991 Judy/Instructo, Minneapolis, MN 55406

Food from the Sea

(Use with page 22.)

People eat food from the sea.

Cut out the paper plate below or use a real one.
Look at page 22.
Cut out the pictures of seafood that you like to eat.
Glue the pictures on the plate.
If you wish, draw
some pictures,
too.

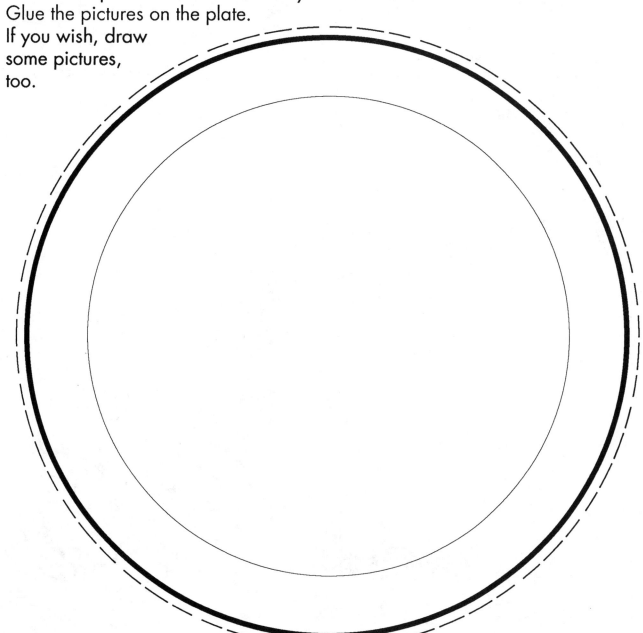

JI 8690 © 1991 Judy/Instructo, Minneapolis, MN 55406

Food from the Sea

(Use with page 21.)

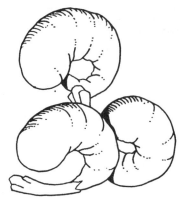

shrimp

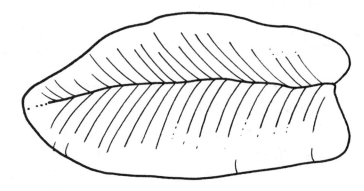

broiled flounder

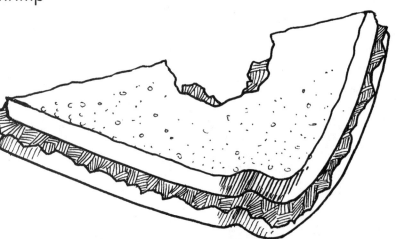

tuna fish sandwich

lobster

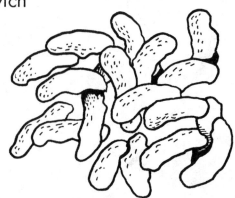

clams

22

JI 8690 © 1991 Judy/Instructo, Minneapolis, MN 55406

Workers of the Sea

The sea provides jobs for people.
This person digs for clams. ⅲ➡

What does this person raise?
Follow the dots A to Z to find out.

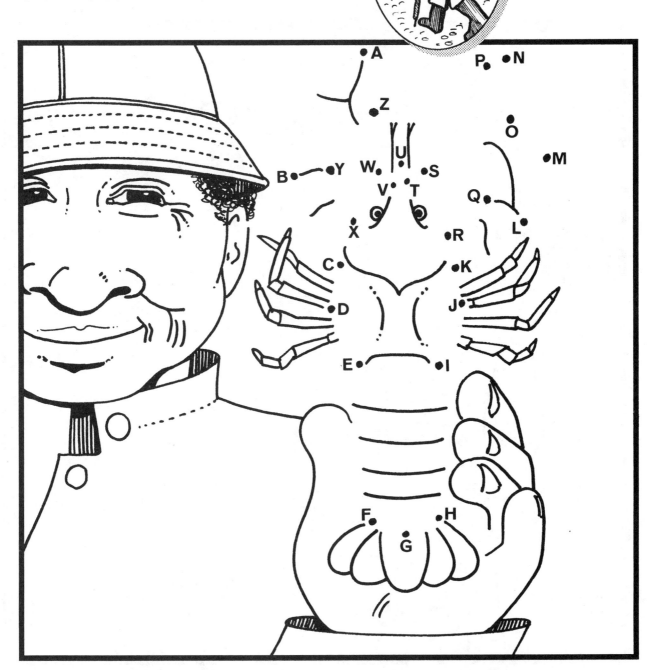

JI 8690 © 1991 Judy/Instructo, Minneapolis, MN 55406

Fun at the Sea

People use the sea for fun.

Help the girl finish the sandcastle.
Color the finished picture.

24

JI 8690 © 1991 Judy/Instructo, Minneapolis, MN 55406

At the Seashore

Did you know that seashells are the homes of many different animals? These are called mollusks.

Say the name of each shell. Trace its name. Then color the shells.

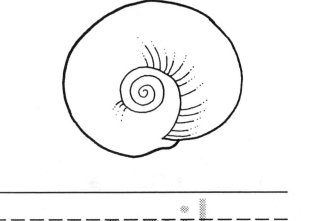

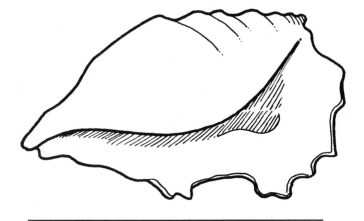

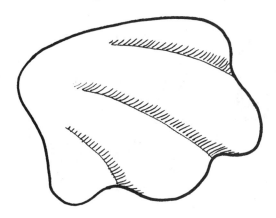

Just for fun!

Say this sentence five times as fast as you can:

Sam and Sally found seashells at the sandy seashore.

JI 8690 © 1991 Judy/Instructo, Minneapolis, MN 55406

Find Their Homes

 This is a hermit crab. It makes its home in empty shells. As it grows it needs to find a bigger and bigger shell. Draw lines to match each shell to the right-sized hermit crab.

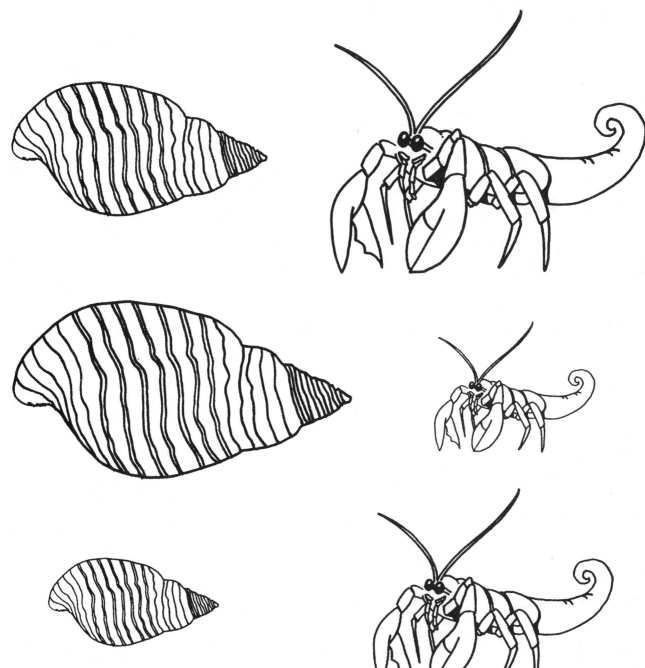

JI 8690 © 1991 Judy/Instructo, Minneapolis, MN 55406

The Big Catch

Many people fish for fun. They take their catch home to share with their families and friends. Who caught the big swordfish? Trace the lines with a pencil to find out.

JI 8690 © 1991 Judy/Instructo, Minneapolis, MN 55406

Fish and Sell

Many people make their living by fishing. They sell the fish to food companies. How many fish are in the fisherman's net?

Circle the number.   **5   10   15   20   25**

Then color the picture.

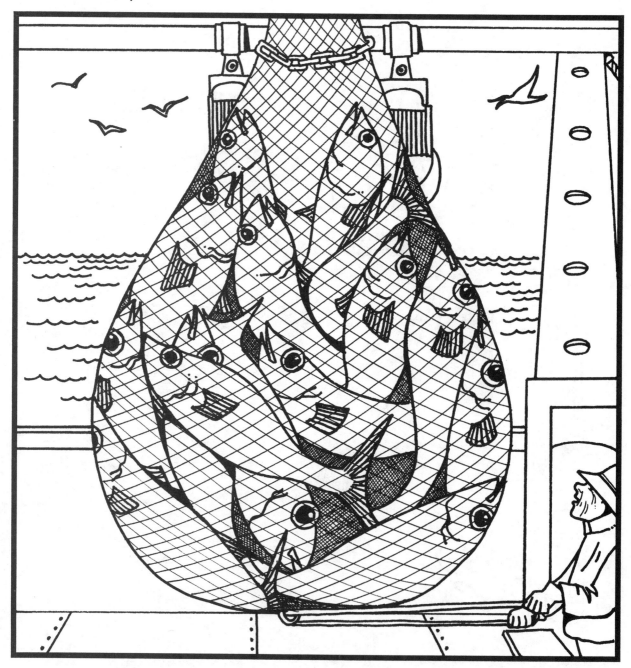

JI 8690 © 1991 Judy/Instructo, Minneapolis, MN 55406

In Port

Large freighters carry goods from port to port.
People are needed to steer the freighters and to keep them running. People also work on the docks loading and unloading the goods.

Color the picture.

JI 8690 © 1991 Judy/Instructo, Minneapolis, MN 55406

Products from the Sea

People take oil and natural gas from the sea. We use oil and gas to run machines, heat our homes and cook our meals.

Cut out each sentence below.

Glue the sentence below the picture it describes.

1. The gasoline helps the car go.

2. The oil helps the bike to work well.

3. Many people have gas stoves.

JI 8690 © 1991 Judy/Instructo, Minneapolis, MN 55406

Read-Listen-Color

Time for Study

People know a lot about the sea. But there is much more to learn. Scientists would like to find out if sealife can be used to make new medicines, and they want to find better ways to remove minerals from the sea.

Scientists and other workers travel to the sea floor. They collect sea urchins, starfish, and other animals and plants so they can study them.

Scientists wear diving suits attached to an oxygen supply. They use an undersea vehicle called a submersible. The submersible has lights attached to it so that the scientists can see in the dark.

Scientists also use undersea robots. The scientists stay in their ship and control the robot's movements. Robots can be made to pick up samples that are in places too deep or too dangerous for divers to enter.

Color the submersible and the robot.

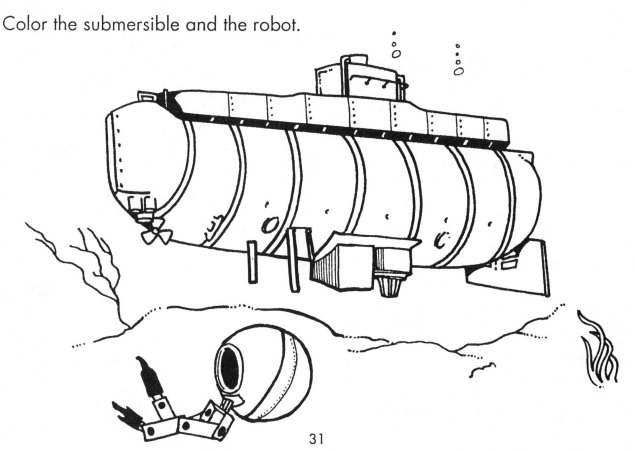

JI 8690 © 1991 Judy/Instructo, Minneapolis, MN 55406

MAMMALS
OF THE SEA

This book belongs to

32

JI 8690 © 1991 Judy/Instructo, Minneapolis, MN 55406

The Humpback Whale

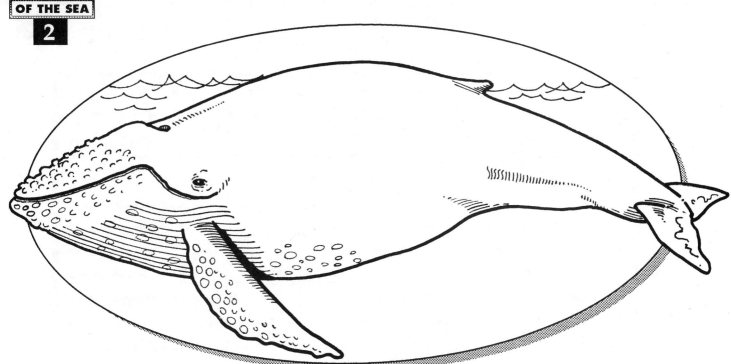

Humpback whales are very large sea animals. Even though they look like big fish, they are mammals. Mammals are warm-blooded animals and use their lungs to breathe. They have hair and give birth to live young called calves. A mother whale nurses her young and cares for her baby during the first year of its life.

Humpbacks travel in groups called pods. As they swim around, they make all kinds of sounds—clicks, groans, and squeaks. These moaning sounds have been called the humpback whale song. Some scientists think whales make these sounds to communicate with one another. The male whales dive deep into the sea, stand on their heads with flippers stretched out, and sing for their mates.

A humpback whale can weigh up to 200 tons. That would be the same weight as 50 semitrailer trucks!

The whale can breathe through a blowhole on top of its head. This whale-breathing looks like a fountain spouting!

JI 8690 © 1991 Judy/Instructo, Minneapolis, MN 55406

The Humpback Whale

Humpback whales are born in warm southern waters. Then they travel long distances to their feeding grounds up north.
Use a pencil. Help the whale go from south to north.

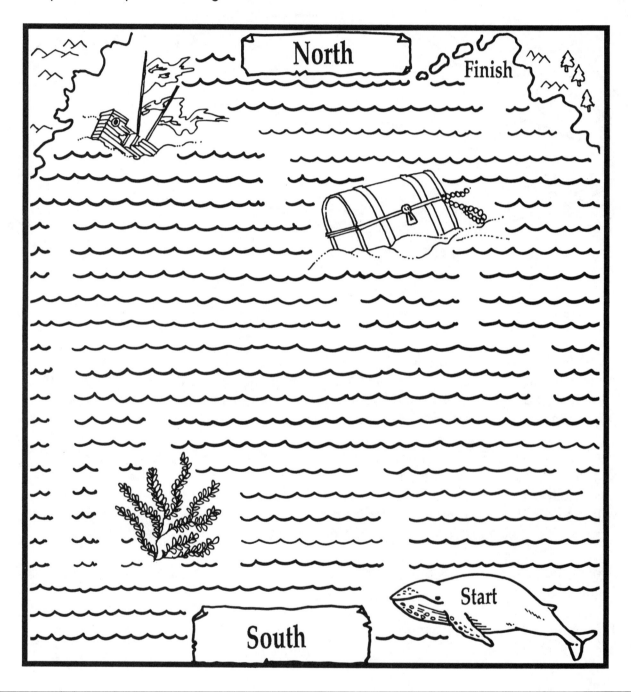

34

JI 8690 © 1991 Judy/Instructo, Minneapolis, MN 55406

The Manatee

The manatee is a large air-breathing mammal that lives in warm shallow waters and eats underwater plants and sea grasses. It has only two legs which are in front, and no hind legs. It also has a tail. Both legs and tail are broad and flat. They look like paddles. The manatee uses them to move through the water.

Manatees are endangered animals. This means they are dying out. Animals sometimes get sick from living in polluted waters. Speedboats often injure the manatees. They also have been hunted for their hide, meat and blubber oil. If the manatees continue to be injured and get sick, they could eventually all die. The United States has laws to protect the manatees. People can go to jail if they harm one of these mammals.

Manatees are sometimes called sea cows because they look like cows grazing. Their babies, born underwater, are called calves. They are very peaceful mammals.

JI 8690 © 1991 Judy/Instructo, Minneapolis, MN 55406

The Manatee

Color every space that has a dot. What do you see?

JI 8690 © 1991 Judy/Instructo, Minneapolis, MN 55406

MAMMALS OF THE SEA

6

The Sea Otter

Sea otters are wonderful acrobats! They like to dive, do somersaults and swim on their backs. Because they are such active mammals, you won't find them sitting still very often.

The sea otter is about four feet long, and has short legs and webbed feet. Their hind feet are used as paddles. This long-bodied animal eats clams, octopuses, crabs, and many other kinds of sea animals and sea urchins. It crushes its food with large, sharp teeth. After eating, the otter can be seen washing itself in the water.

The mother otter holds her baby, called a pup, on her chest as she floats and paddles around. It's amazing that the sea otter can sleep and eat while lying on its back in the ocean!

Sea otters have beautiful brown and gray-tipped fur. Once hunted in large numbers for their fur, they almost died out. But now there are laws to protect them from being harmed.

JI 8690 © 1991 Judy/Instructo, Minneapolis, MN 55406

The Sea Otter

Find and color the large sea otter that looks exactly like this small one.

JI 8690 © 1991 Judy/Instructo, Minneapolis, MN 55406

The Sea Lion

The sea lion is one kind of seal. It has small ears and flippers. The four flippers help the animal to move both on land and in the water. They are graceful mammals and have no trouble leaping over steep slopes and big rocks on the shoreline. Sea lions eat fish, squid and shellfish. They are known to be good fishermen which means they can catch their food easily.

The sea lion babies are called pups and are born on land. The pups are born one at a time and are brown at birth, unlike other seals which are born black. Sea lion pups are good swimmers and like to play in the water.

Sea lions live in large groups, called herds, on rocky shores of the ocean. They are extremely sociable and like living close together. They are tame animals and allow people to get close to them.

Sea lions are often trained to be in animal shows and are wonderful acrobats. They seem to have a naturally playful spirit and learn to perform tricks easily. Maybe you have seen one balance a ball on its nose or "clap" its flippers.

JI 8690 © 1991 Judy/Instructo, Minneapolis, MN 55406

The Sea Lion

Color the sea lion, the ball, the fish and the stand.
Cut them out.
Glue the sea lion on the stand.
Glue the ball on the sea lion's nose.
Glue the fish in the sea lion's mouth.

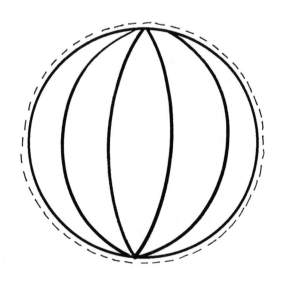

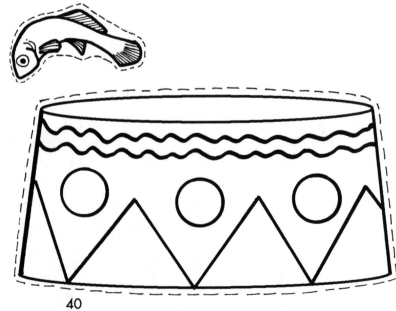

40

JI 8690 © 1991 Judy/Instructo, Minneapolis, MN 55406

The Walrus

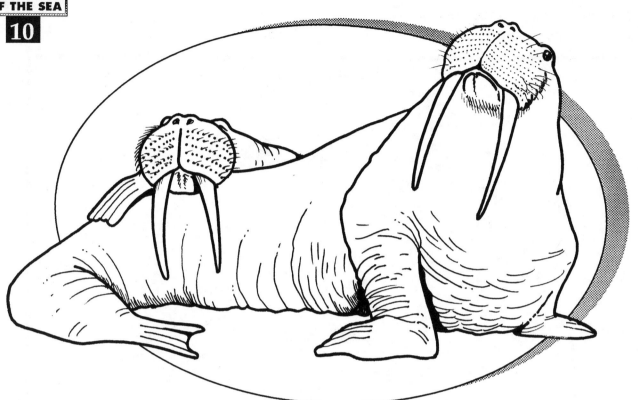

The walrus is a big mammal with a bristly mustache and two long white tusks. This wrinkly mammal is related to the sea lion and the seal. The male walrus is larger than the female and can weigh as much as two tons: A small car weighs one ton so you can compare the walrus to two compact cars!

A walrus' tusks are really two very large teeth. They are an important part of the walrus' body. For example, the walrus uses its tusks to rake the ocean bottom for shellfish. They dig for clams, crabs and snails to eat. The tusks are also used as hooks to help the walrus lift itself onto a sheet of ice. A walrus may be seen using its tusks as weapons to fight off enemies, such as the polar bear. Some tusks are three feet long!

You may see a group of 100 walruses lying together on large pieces of ice, called ice floes, or rocky shores with their tusks resting on each other. Like the sea lions, walruses are happy living in their crowded herds. Walrus babies are born on the ice floes and can swim immediately after birth. They like to hold on to their mothers for the first few weeks as they learn to swim better and dive.

JI 8690 © 1991 Judy/Instructo, Minneapolis, MN 55406

The Walrus

Color the walrus brown or black.
Cut out the the tusks and glue them on the walrus' face.

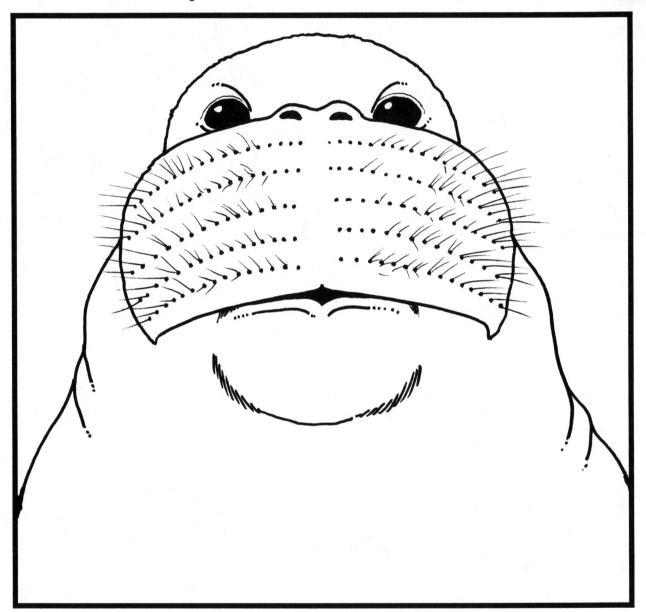

42

JI 8690 © 1991 Judy/Instructo, Minneapolis, MN 55406

The Dolphin

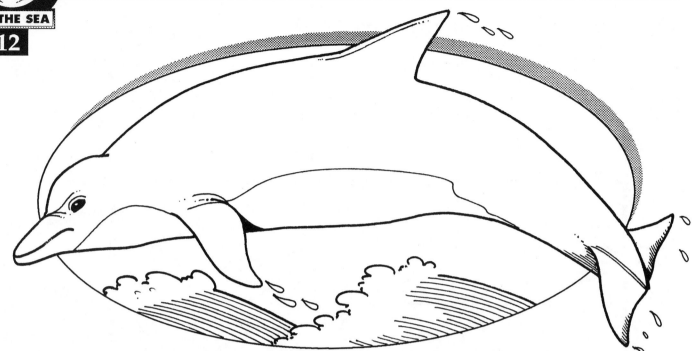

The dolphin is a kind of whale. It is a beautiful and graceful mammal. This playful, sleek animal has a long narrow snout and a smooth body. It has flippers and a tail. The dolphin likes to live in large groups, called schools, in shallow waters in the ocean. They feed on squid and other fish.

Dolphins are very good swimmers. For some reason, they often swim above schools of tuna. Sometimes they get caught in fishermen's nets and cannot get to the surface of the water to breathe.

For many years people who want to protect the dolphins have written letters to lawmakers. They have made posters and written stories about how the dolphins were being harmed by driftnets. These people have made a difference! Many tuna fishermen in the United States have agreed to use fishing lines instead of nets to catch tuna. Then the dolphins can swim around safely and enjoy themselves.

Like the humpback whales, dolphins talk to each other by making sounds. They have excellent hearing and can sense danger by the sounds they hear. Dolphins like to leap out of the water and somersault in the air. They are easily trained to do tricks. Sometimes they make up their own tricks by watching other dolphins! It's fun to watch dolphins perform.

JI 8690 © 1991 Judy/Instructo, Minneapolis, MN 55406

How Many Dolphins? How Many Fish?

Count the dolphins. Circle the number of dolphins that you see.

1   **2**   **3**   **4**   **5**

Count the fish. Circle the number of fish that you see.

6   **7**   **8**   **9**   **10**

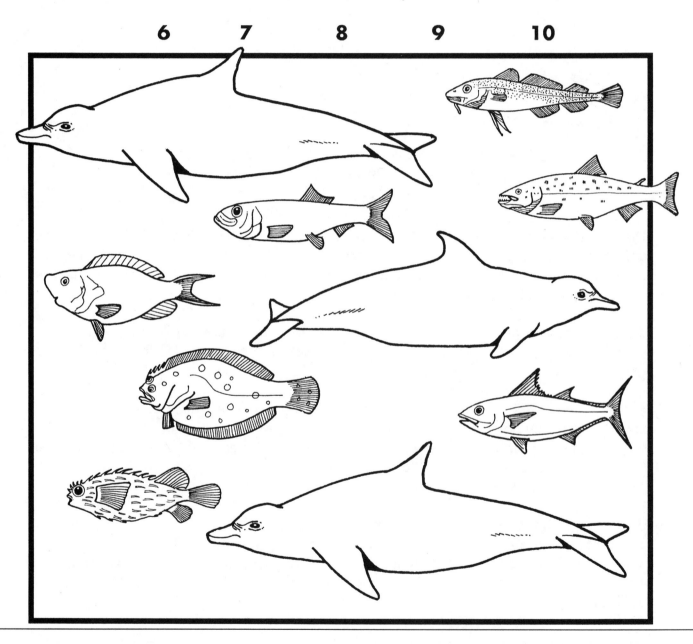

JI 8690 © 1991 Judy/Instructo, Minneapolis, MN 55406

Sea Animal Cutouts

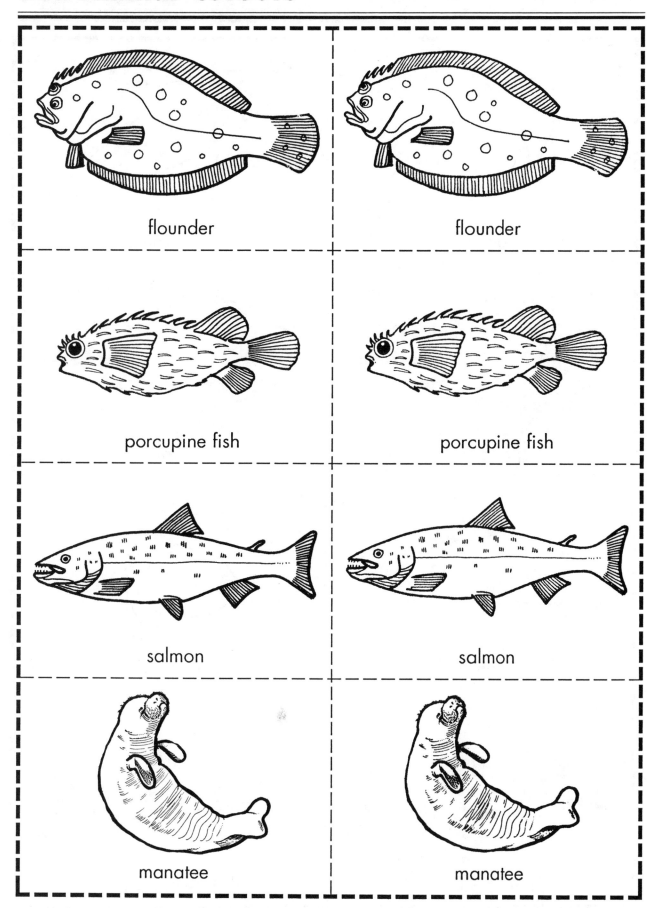

flounder

flounder

porcupine fish

porcupine fish

salmon

salmon

manatee

manatee

45

JI 8690 © 1991 Judy/Instructo, Minneapolis, MN 55406

Sea Animal Cutouts

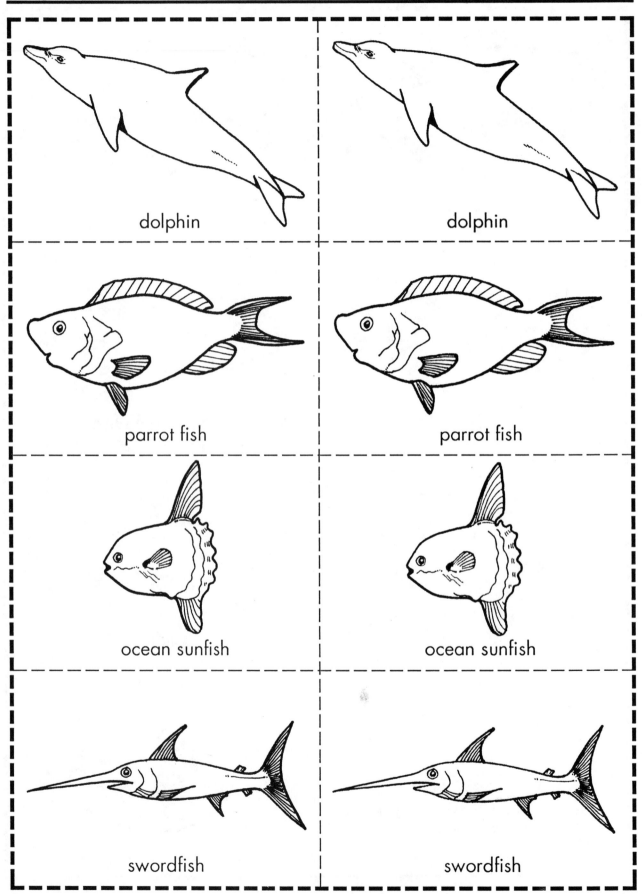

dolphin

dolphin

parrot fish

parrot fish

ocean sunfish

ocean sunfish

swordfish

swordfish

46

JI 8690 © 1991 Judy/Instructo, Minneapolis, MN 55406

Sea Animal Cutouts

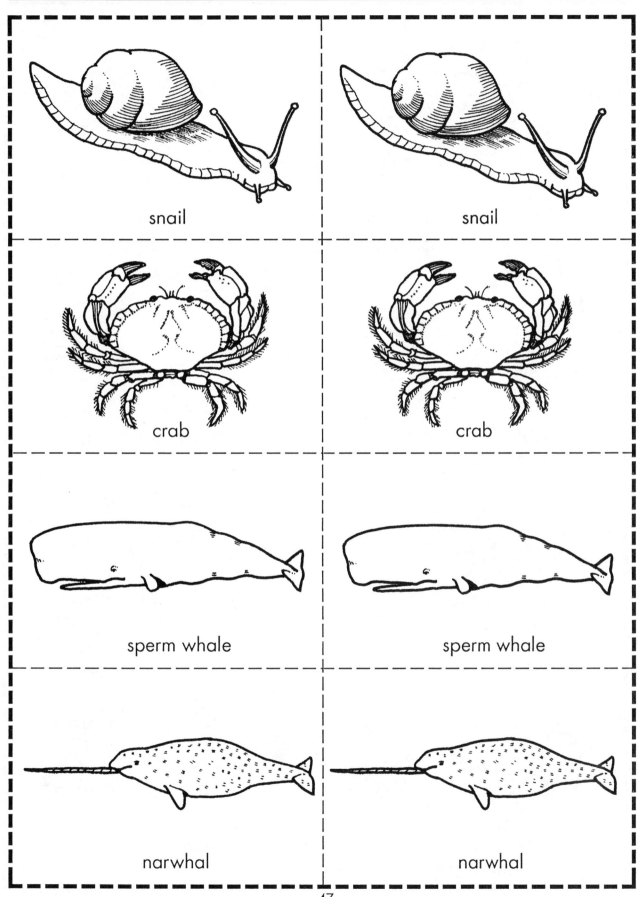

snail

snail

crab

crab

sperm whale

sperm whale

narwhal

narwhal

JI 8690 © 1991 Judy/Instructo, Minneapolis, MN 55406

Sea Animal Cutouts

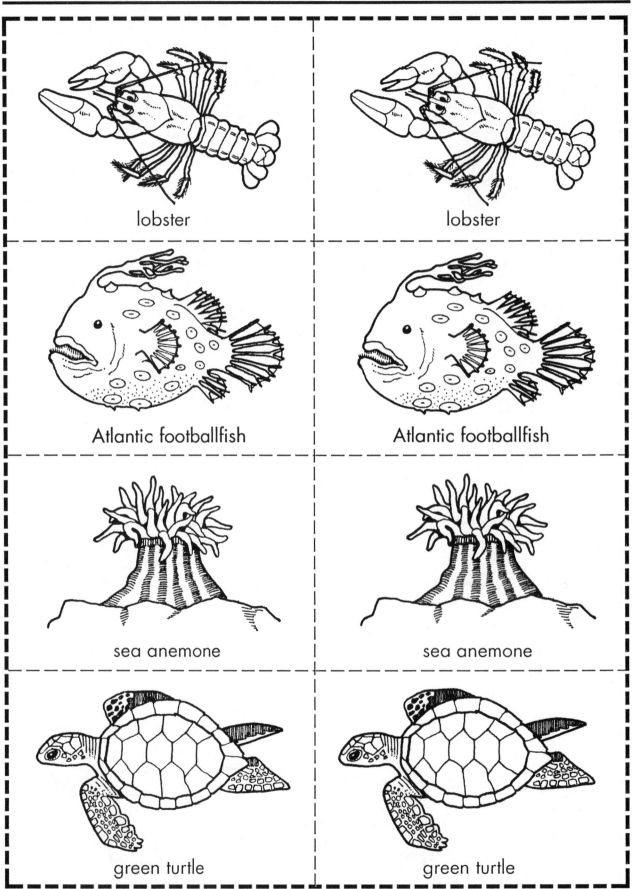

lobster

lobster

Atlantic footballfish

Atlantic footballfish

sea anemone

sea anemone

green turtle

green turtle

48

JI 8690 © 1991 Judy/Instructo, Minneapolis, MN 55406